The Best Cartoons from
Leadership *Journal*

Volume 5

"It's showtime, baby!"

The Best Cartoons from
Leadership
Journal

Volume 5

BROADMAN
& HOLMAN
PUBLISHERS

Nashville, Tennessee

Published by Broadman & Holman Publishers,
Nashville, Tennessee
Editorial Team: Leonard G. Goss, John Landers

0-8054-2156-4

Dewey Decimal Classification: 817
Subject Heading: HUMOR

01 02 03 04 05 04 03 02 01 00

The Baptism

1

"I think it's time we all pitched in
and bought some new choir robes."

© 1993 John McPherson

"It's her way of telling us the
music budget is in a squeeze."

"Before our special music this morning, I'd like to remind you of the organ repair fund."

"Our insurance doesn't cover
candle-lighting services anymore."

"I know the pizza house gave you a good price,
but I still prefer the old choir."

"There's one other problem I'd like to discuss."

"My friends, I'm sorry to harp
on the pulpit restoration fund, but . . ."

"Rose, where's that shoestring
you always say we're operating on?"

"Pastor, any word yet on our
fund drive for office improvements?"

"Pastor, they say that putting a copier log on the machine helps reduce personal use."

" . . . and this is your pastoral Stewardship Center."

"Good news! We've decided to start
a fund drive for office improvements."

13

"The board didn't approve your idea of purchasing you
a cellular phone, but compromises were made."

Subliminal Preaching

© 1983 Erik and Vicki Johnson

"My congregation took up an offering for my continuing education. Know of any conferences for $7.22?"

"The board gave me $100 toward my $200 round-trip to the conference."

17

"What do you mean, in lieu of a salary increase you'd prefer Sundays off?"

18

"And most important, be nice to
the treasurer and his wife."

Pastor and Mrs. Wilson should have guessed that the congregation's offer of doubled salary, two-month vacations, and every fourth weekend free was less than sincere.

"The pastor always manages to make
his financial needs very clear to us."

21

"Actually, the secret to my fortune is that every time I received a phone call that began, 'Pastor, I know this is your day off, but . . .' I put $10 in my savings."

"We feel your compensation should be the same as the
average church member . . . as long as the average
church member doesn't make over $17,500."

"About my salary—as it was in the beginning, and is now . . . so shall it be evermore?"

"Whatever we decide about the pastor's salary,
let's keep in mind all those sermons last
year on the simple lifestyle."

25

"Hi, Pastor. We were just talking about
your request for a salary increase."

26

"No wonder I hate visitation!"

"Due to this month's budget problems,
we can't afford your usual check, but we do
have an equivalent in recyclable aluminum cans."

"I was really excited when they told me I'd make $400 a week. Then I found out that meant $7 an hour!"

"The board agreed that you're worth your weight in gold,
but we can afford your weight in aluminum."

Pastor-turned-ventriloquist Edgar Smylie debuts
at the Friday night business meeting.

"We've finished the budget, and I'm afraid you're going to have to tighten your belt a little bit more."

"The bad news is we turned down your cost-of-living raise. The good news is that you're now eligible for assistance from our Food Pantry."

"Rev. Greer refuses to negotiate . . .
he said we should talk to his agent."

"Looks like the pastor got his pay raise!"

"And in appreciation of our retiring pastor, we'd like to give him this offering as a little momentum."

"Your stewardship sermons are improving.
Still no money, but a lot more IOUs."

"It was a nice sermon, but it seems to me that you have committed the Lord to more than he may wish to do for the economy."

"Well, actually, the sermon didn't quite fit my needs.
Where do I go to get a refund on my offering?"

"I realize salvation is free . . . but what is the suggested donation?"

41

"Welcome!"

"So, I'd like to begin a ten-part series on stewardship."

"It happens every time he mentions church finances."

"That was the best sermon on giving I've ever heard."

"Let's go over my sermon again. Surely
I must have said something."

"We need fifteen thousand big ones. No questions asked."

© 1992 Rob Portlock

"Gimme a 'T' . . . Gimme an 'I' . . . Gimme a 'T-H-E' . . ."

Wilbur Bellew. One man ushering crew.

"I wrote the music for an offertory, which when played backwards, you hear, 'Tithe, tithe; it feels good to tithe.'"

50

"I guess we know what the pastor's going to preach about today."

53

"The nicest thing I can say about the
financial report is that it's time to make
Malachi 3:10 the Sunday morning text again."

55

"We go to the generic church . . . the tithe is only 9%"

"Since we put in a 'Non-Tithing' section,
tithing has increased 50 percent."

"Yeah, it brings in a lot of people, but they all want 2.9 percent tithing."

"Suppose we return your tithes, give you a
reserved parking place, make you an elder, fire
the youth minister, and eliminate the music
committee. Would that be satisfactory?"

"After three weeks of enjoying the church's services, prayer, fellowship, and counseling, I still feel a deep spiritual yearning. So I'm going to sue your socks off."

61

"Blue minivan, license number XYZ-100. You've left your lights on, and you've fallen behind on your stewardship pledge, year to date."

"I suppose promises of moral support would not suffice?"

Church choir director Denzel Brainard knew
how to recruit choir participants.

"He's always nice, but I know he's thinking—
'This kid gave only $1.23 last year.'"

Jackie Rivers, former Hollywood agent,
makes his deacon debut

"Way to go, Chuck, baby! Your sermon cost
$75.83 to put together, and you grossed $2,712!
You did it, kid. You're beautiful!"

"Our TitheVision board seems to
be working out well, Fred."

67

"They have a way of singling out non-tithers."

"Based on early reports from two ushers
and the church treasurer, we are projecting
this morning's offering to be $5,917.02."

"It's showtime, baby!"

"Two collection plates are still out there somewhere."

"I'm going to invest in copper futures."

Taking a cue from John Madden, Pastor Mel
diagrams the morning offering for the ushers.

"Hello. My name is Brad, and I'll be your usher this morning."

"I believe we've met our deductible."

"It's those credit-check calls that slow everything down."

"I think it's about time somebody told Mrs. Nurlspar
we don't accept deposit soda cans for the offering."

"Gesundheit."

"I'm sorry, Reverend, but we do not give
clergy discounts on the Indiana Toll Road."

© 1994 Chris Kalton

"Before our morning offering, we'll take
a few quiet moments for you to use the ATM
we recently installed in the back of the church."

The new "Insta-Tithe" made giving a snap!

"Do you suppose the Finance Committee
is trying to tell us something?"

"We're not all that sold on the theology
of the thing, but we do like the results."

83

"That's what I like about him . . . innovation!"

"Pew for two near the back."

"I don't like the looks of this."

"Besides being highly educational,
it's boosted our offering by 85 percent!"

Usher Ed "Ten Dollar Minimum" Smith

"It looks like an offering we can't refuse."

Church consultants from Southern California

"It's my latest invention! This offering plate will ring a little bell if you put in $20 . . . if you don't put in anything, it takes your picture!"

"It solves our usher problem."

"Offerings . . . Ushers . . . Minimum age thereof . . .
I'm sure it's in here somewhere!"

94

"The board voted not to increase staff salaries, but instead to permit commercial endorsements."

"We made $125 on the chili supper and
$231 at the antacid stand."

"Then it's settled. We announce a paper drive, preferably green ones with Abe Lincoln's picture on them."

"They're not going to believe this back home!"

"Oh, nothing in particular. But, hey, you never know
when you might need some additional funds."

99

"The finance committee hired a consultant."

"Don't think of it as estate planning. In these troubled times, think of it as creative tithing."

© 1998 Dan Pegoda

"While renting has its advantages, it is the opinion
of the deacons that we start a building fund."

"The good news is that the building fund drive is right on schedule. The bad news is that the architect informs us that the target amount is completely inadequate."

"The Flock is coming through on the building fund drive, but not without a good deal of bleating."

105

"Since the building fund won't cover a Crystal Cathedral, how about a Timber Temple?"

"As far as the new building goes, we're still trying to narrow the gulf between what we'd like and what we can afford."

Plans For the New Church Building As Seen By . .

the youth pastor

The music director

The church secretary

The pastor

The finance committee

"Are we glad to hear that you don't know where you'll get the money for the building fund! For a minute there we were afraid you wanted to get it from us."

"No, I don't think we could call the building fund drive a success in the literal sense."

" . . . another pledge for the building fund drive."

"The difficult question was, how badly
did we need this new building?"

"And if the denomination wants to keep the property?"

"It's hard to believe all this came from a mustard seed."

"We ran out of money right after we built the pulpit."

"Must be for the building fund."

"This is a most generous donation, Mr. Burgess. I thank you, the church thanks you, and if your unconfessed sin is still unbearable next week, feel free to give again."

"I'll trade you two young couples for a tither at the peak of his earning potential."

© 1990 Doug Hall

"I don't care how needy they are, Rev. Casey.
You just can't claim your congregation as
'three hundred codependents.'"

"Any word yet, Pastor, about my request for a photocopier?"

After 29 years of service, church secretary Marge
Feldern hands the reins over to Ellen Fetz.

"He does this every winter to make us think they haven't turned the thermostat down."

"Our choice seems to be between sending a missionary and installing new carpet in the catacombs."

"Let's see . . . I'll take better, richer, and, hmmmmm, in health."

Pastor Greer's attempt to raise his youth group's consciousness of Third World poverty was not entirely successful.

"Waterskiing ministry: $200, fast-food evangelism: $375,
cinema ministry: $95, amusement part outreach: $130,
pizza parlor discipleship: $185 . . . Say, look here—
books—$75! Are we paying this guy to read?"

"First, the good news . . . the youth raised the
money to go to camp this year. Now, the bad . . .
they did it by selling the church van."

"I'd like to introduce our new Irving T. Hunsbreath Memorial Youth Pastor."

"Cheer up! Most youth pastors don't receive ANY housing allowance."

"The chairman of the board took your youth group while you were ill. I think you're getting a raise!"

"They're 'casting lots' to see who goes with the junior high kids to camp."

131

"Either this is an illustrated sermon
on the Good Shepherd, or the pastor's
getting up another trip to the Holy Land."

"You and your cut-rate trips to the Holy Land!"

It was the Sunday that Pastor Otterblat decided to put his foot down against nursery number pools.

The new technology led to greater
efficiency at First Church.

"I don't care who broke down the walls of Jericho!
I move that we pay for it out of the general fund
and charge it up to miscellaneous."

"The financial report, brought to you in living color—red."

"Now, as your treasurer, when I talk about our going into Chapter 11, I'm not talking about the book of Matthew."

"I'm beginning to think that $17 billion faith pledge was a hoax!"

"Giving has been a little erratic this quarter."

"He was working on the church budget, but then he found the 'Schismatic Invaders' game."

"Approving this year's budget may be a little tougher than we thought."

"Call me old-fashioned, but do we
really need 3-D sermons?"

The church newsletter committee
presents a bold concept to the board.

"It's a little extravagant, but it seems to put the couples at ease to discuss their personal problems."

"He's insisted on that ramp ever
since he visited Atlantic City."

The congregation began dropping subtle
hints that they wanted pew cushions.

"Now, that's what I call church!"

"What worries me is that this model cost more to build than the present church did."

Pastor Cox has second thoughts about
the money saved by having the men's group,
rather professionals, install the electric
heater in the baptistery.

"I'm sorry, Reverend Greer, but the board just vetoed your proposal to increase defense spending."

© 1985 Doug Hall

"This year our special Christmas offering will go to cover damages and lawsuits resulting from the donkey running amuck at our living Nativity."

"Rev. Smith, would you ask your family to wait outside?"

"Reverend, this is the Internal Revenue Service. Can you confirm that Mr. Jones gave $2,306 to your church last year?"

"If he hasn't yet, I can guarantee he will."

"I'd like you to meet Irving R. Simmons. He's heading up our stewardship drive, and we thought a nice, monogrammed briefcase would make his job easier."